Contents

All about animals

Hello!	4-5
Warming Up	6-7
Off we go!	8-9
Moving!	10-11
Playing together	12-13
Musical games	14-15
A moment to listen	16-17
A lullaby, shhh ...	18-19
Goodbye!	20-21

All about water

Hello again!	22-23
Warming Up	24-25
Off we go!	26-27
Moving!	28-29
Playing together	30-31
Musical games	32-33
A moment to listen	34-35
A lullaby, shhh ...	36-37
Goodbye!	38-39

Musical Resources

Very young children benefit from the experience of playing and singing along with the highest quality percussive instruments to explore the different sounds they make. Musical activities can be just as fun to use at home as in a nursery environment.

In Little Birdsong **Two** you will come across many pictures showing the loveliest instruments for young children. Toddlers and young children can play them, and explore a wide range of sounds and textures.
They can be sourced through www.littlebirdsong.co.uk

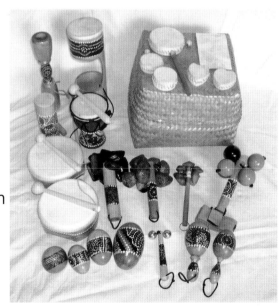

Hot tips to try

Wherever you are in the world, Little Birdsong **Two** is for young children to enjoy musical experiences together. The music has been composed to encompass repetition, memory recall, catchy melodies and different styles. Whether singing, dancing or simply listening, the words are supported by whimsical illustrations to help children to understand their English meaning.

Little Birdsong **Two** has joy at its heart and an understanding of music from a child's perspective. Young children can make choices, speak English and musically engage. Ideas are thoughtfully woven into compositions, and encourage family engagement as well as independent enjoyment.

As a trusted adult, parents already have vital skills to help encourage vocalising and musical engagement. Singing new songs together is both enriching and fun. Routine activities such as washing or tidying up become much more interesting with music making.

A few quality musical times together will create giant leaps in learning, aesthetic appreciation, parental bonding and self-motivation. Give your child time to absorb what is heard, and to sing when ready. Repeat words from the songs at different times of the day and encourage your child to respond. Hum a melody and see what happens. By challenging and musically building on what they know, children will experiment with new words through singsong and musical play.

0-2yrs

Babies and toddlers absorb what they hear, what they see and what they feel. Their life experiences are embedded through their immediate environment into their tiny bodies and senses. Do use a slightly slower tempo to move and sing. Give them lots of time to listen, and see how they respond. In dancing and bouncing activities support a baby's neck where necessary. Given time and space in musical engagement, babies and toddlers will astonish families with their ability to decipher musical ideas, and to be spontaneous in response - often when least expected.

As they grow and develop babies will begin to utter babbly sounds. This makes perfect sense to a parent. Adult participation is vital to encourage vocalisation and awareness in a baby's musical experiences. They have a compelling depth of memory retention, and in time when ready, toddlers will repeat new words naturally. Shared musical experience in young children through resources such as Little Birdsong Two will provide a foundation for vocalising, and helps to feed the creative pathways in a child's overall life.

2-4yrs

This age group is hungry to learn, and eager to demonstrate new skills and achievement. Musical play helps them to explore and practice new words and sounds in their daily lives.

This age group is quick to respond verbally, and although tempting to speed the learning process up, children will repeat new words musically if given the space and time to absorb. Young children love to be challenged, and by building on the special songs that they learn, children will be empowered. Within musical activities they are compelled to try new words without the educational pressure so often attached to literacy and reading.

Children really appreciate their loved adults joining in. By creating a musical environment with quality instruments, simple props, or even just making their own sounds, young children will have a lovely time trying new words, songs and musical games. Join in, watch, support and above all embrace musical spontaneity. The rewards will undoubtedly be enriching, and enhance everyone's musical learning.

Hello!

Try this ...

1-2 yrs
◆ Sway gently sideways with lots of waves

◆ Enjoy the actions together as described

2-4 yrs
◆ Make a house shape using your hands.

◆ Wave hands hello.
 Once familiar with words suggest,
"What shall we do now?"

4

In our house, our music house,
Singing and dancing, play the instruments.
In our house, our music house,
Happy happy musical time.

Sing hello together, together, together.
Sing hello together, sing hello.
Pat your head together ...
Clap your hands together ...
Tickle your tummy together ....
Stamp your feet together ...

5

Warming up

Try this ...

1-2 yrs
◆ Lift babies up high on "fly".
Help toddlers "flap" their, arms.
Lift them up on "swoop".
Wiggle them on "waddle".
Nod heads together on "nod".

2-4 yrs
◆ Encourage independent action and singing.
Each child has a go at "flying" round.
Use a puppet to help the children to move and sing.
Replace "blue bird" with another colour.

Blue bird, blue bird, flap your wings, flap your wings, flap your wings.
Blue bird, blue bird flap your wings, flap your wings and fly.

Blue bird, blue bird, swoop up high, swoop down low, swoop up high.

Blue bird, blue bird, swoop up high,
... Flap your wings and fly.

Blue bird, blue bird waddle your bottom...
...Flap your wings and fly.

Blue bird, blue bird nod your head...
...Flap your wings and fly.

Blue bird, blue bird, flap your wings, flap your wings, flap your wings.
Blue bird, blue bird flap your wings, flap your wings and fly.

7

Off we go!

Woof woof woof woof

Try this ...

1-2 yrs

◆ Parents sing together and wave to all babies on "Hey-ho".
Tickle child on animal sounds.

2-4 yrs

◆ As a seated group in a circle:
Sing together and clap with "Hey-ho".
Encourage independent sounds, singing and movement.
A child walks around the circle making the sound
and movement of the animal.

Oink

Neighhhhhhh

The farmer's on the farm, the farmer's on the farm,
Hey-ho, Hey-ho,
The farmer's on the farm.

The farmer wants a dog, the farmer wants a dog,
Woof, woof, woof, woof the farmer wants a dog.

The dog wants a cat, the dog wants a cat,
Meow, meow, the dog wants a cat.

The cat wants a mouse (eek, eek)
The mouse wants a pig (oink, oink)
The pig wants a cow (moo moo)
The cow wants a horse (neigh, neigh)
The horse wants a sheep (baa, baa)

The sheep wants to sleep, the sheep wants to sleep,
Shhh, shhh the sheep wants to sleep.
S h h h h h h!

Moving!

Try this ...

1-2 yrs
◆ Walk together in time to the beat.
Keep still at the end of the song.
Turn in any direction.
Walk together as before.
Continue together as suggested.

2-4 yrs
◆ Encourage independent singing and moving.
Use a percussion instrument, make a
funny sound to turn around.
Continue moving as suggested.

◆ Talk about animals that make similar movements.
Explore their sounds and the way that they move.

Walking on the green grass, green grass, green grass.
Walking on the green grass, early in the morning.

Running... *jumping* ...Walking

Can you find a partner, a partner, a partner.
Can you find a partner, we're turning all around... *Weeeeeeeee!*

Clip clop goes the pony, the pony, the pony.
Clip clop goes the pony, early in the morning.

Galloping galloping galloping galloping ...

Early in the morning. Neigh!

11

Playing together

Try this ...

1-2 yrs

◆ Place a basket of instruments on the floor.

Encourage toddlers to come forward whilst singing.

◆ Allow toddlers to play as you sing.

Have a moment of quiet at the end of the song.

Sing again, quietly or loudly.

◆ Encourage sound making with instruments or voices.

2-4 yrs

◆ Create a basket of things that make a sound such as bells and spoons.

Pass the basket round to the song.

Everyone chooses an instrument and plays together.

One child chooses an instrument at the end of the first verse.

Everyone listens to its sound & learns the instrument name.

◆ Play in time to the song. Enjoy a quiet moment then play again.

◆ Explore different sounds made by the instruments and your voice.

Pass the instruments around, pass them all around.
Pass the instruments around, do not make a sound.

Can you hear the instruments, can you hear the sound?
Can you hear the instruments, as they move around.

Can you choose an instrument, can you hear the sound.
Can you choose an instrument, as they move around.

Play together play along.
Play together play along.

Shaka shaka shaka shaka shaka shaka shaka shake

Play together play along.

The mouse crept through the house ...

The cat jumped over the chair ...
The dog ran into the woods ...
The pig rolled over and over ...
The horse galloped in the field ...
The farmer milked the cow ...

Musical games

Try this ...

1-2 yrs

◆ Bounce toddlers up and down.
Walk your fingers up their legs.
Rock from side to side.
Stop moving and clap hands on "SNAP".
Tickle baby.

◆ Enjoy song 2 as with song 1.

2-4 yrs

◆ Wiggle one hand.
The other hand moves like a crocodile.
Wiggle one hand again.
Clap hands once, loudly.
Wiggle a finger for the monkey.
Rub tummy on "mmmmm!"

◆ Enjoy song 2 as with song 1.

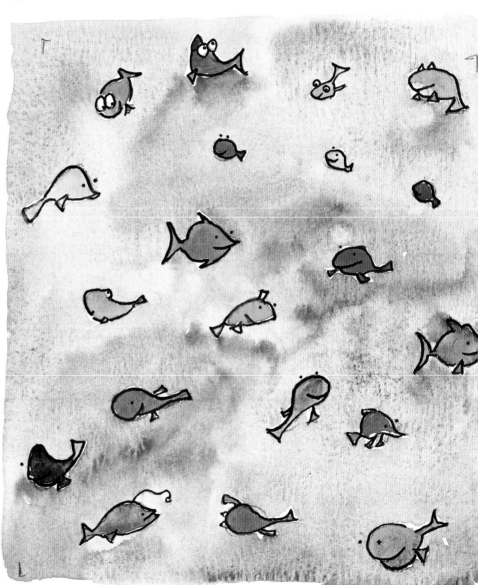

5 little monkeys sitting in a tree
Along came a crocodile as quiet as can be.
Hey Mr Crocodile you can't catch me!
"SNAP!" 1 little monkey for my tea.
How many were left? 1, 2, 3, 4!
No more monkeys for my tea.

mmmm**mm**

5 small fish swimming in the sea.
Along came a big fish quiet as can be.
Hey Mr Big Fish, you can't catch me.
"SNAP!" 1 small fish for my tea.
How many were left?   1, 2, 3, 4!
No more small fish for my tea.

mmm**mmm**

A moment to listen

Try this ...

Clementi's Sonatina in G on piano

1-2 yrs
◆ Enjoy listening, to the music together.
◆ Pretend to play the piano and see how they respond.

2-4 yrs
◆ Listen to the music together.
◆ Play it again and ask questions such as,
"What can you hear?"
"Is it happy/sad?"
"Is it fast/slow?"
"Play the piano when you hear it" - encourage them to pretend.

◆ Cut out smiley and sad faces on card, and ask children to choose
one after the music has played.

A lullaby, shhh...

Try this ...

1-2 yrs
◆ Listen to the song together.
◆ Now sing "twitwoo" when you hear it.
Sing and pretend your hand is an owl.
Put hands up high for the stars and the moon.

2-4 yrs
◆ A child walks round as the owl.
The group sings "Where is the owl?"
The owl sings "twitwoo" and keeps walking
throughout the song.
Another child is chosen to be the owl.
◆ A puppet owl will help the child to sing

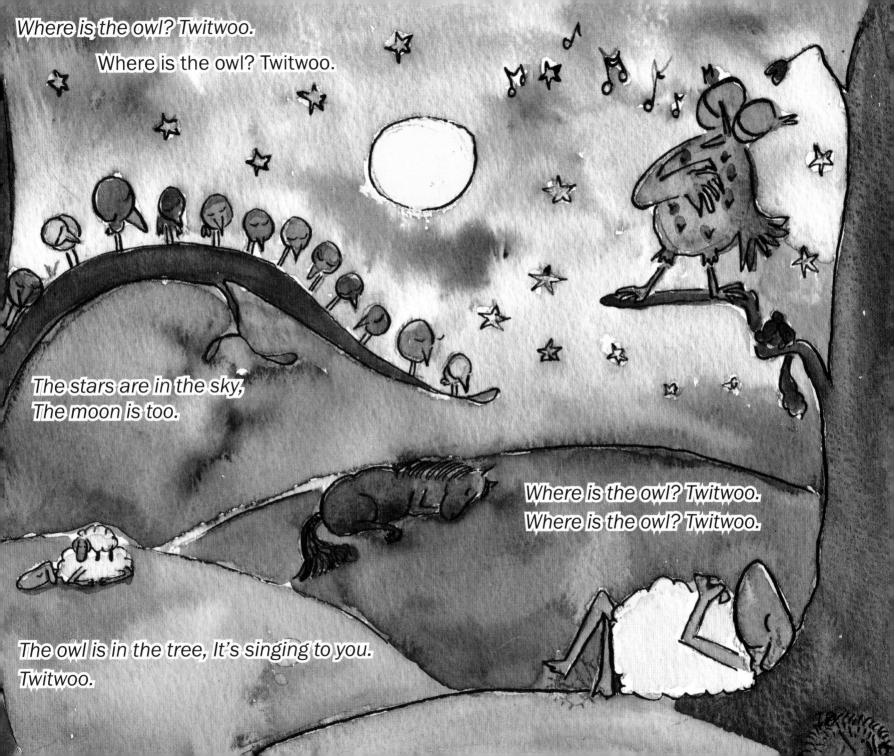

Goodbye!

Try this ...

1-2 yrs
◆ *Sway gently sideways whilst waving.*
Sing goodbye to each child.

2-4 yrs
◆ *Sing together whilst waving.*
Sing goodbye to each child.

bye!

bye!

bye!

bye!

20

Goodbye!

Sing goodbye together, together, together.
Sing goodbye together, sing goodbye.

Clap your hands together, together, together.
Clap your hands together, clap goodbye.

Sing goodbye together, together, together.
Sing goodbye together, sing goodbye.

bye bye!

21

Hello again!

Try this ...

1-2 yrs
- ◆ Sway gently sideways for hello.

- ◆ Encourage actions as described.

2-4 yrs
- ◆ Encourage singing and actions together.

- ◆ Sing hello to each child.

Ask, "What action shall we do now?"

In our house, our music house,
Singing and dancing, play the instruments.
In our house, our music house,
Happy happy musical time.

Sing hello, hello, Sing hello, hello,
Sing hello, hello to you.
Can you pat your head, can you pat your head,
can you pat your head, hello.
Can you clap your hands, can you clap your hands...
Can you tap your toes, can you tap your toes...
Can you shake everything,
can you shake everything...

Warming Up

Try this ...

1-2 yrs

◆ Wiggle fingers with first line.
Tickle tummy and tickle hair.
Wiggle baby's arms gently up then wiggle baby's arms gently down.
Count lots of 'bubbles' with gentle prods on baby's tummy.

◆ When you count "1 bubble", wiggle 1 finger, then 2, and so on.

2-4 yrs

◆ Make big bubble shapes with your hands, then 'blow' it away.
Choose some children to be a bubble.
The other children sing and blow the 'bubbles' around.
They then change places.

◆ Encourage independent movement and sound-making with water and bubbly sounds!

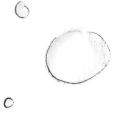

Bubbles (blow), bubbles (blow), bubbles everywhere (blow).
Bubbles on my tummy, bubbles in my hair.
Bubbles up high, bubbles down low.
How many bubbles can you blow?

1 bubble (blow)
2 bubbles (blow)
3 bubbles (blow)

Water in the air – WOOSH
Water in the sea – SWISH
Water, water, everywhere,

But not on ME. **SPLASH!**

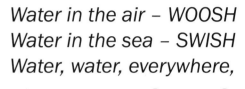

Off we go!

Try this ...

1-2 yrs
◆ Bounce baby gently up and down.
On line 3, sway the baby side to side.
One line 5, push baby gently round.
Bounce up and down again
Make lots of "mmmm" sounds.

2-4 yrs
◆ Make fish shapes with hands.
Hold a 'rod' and wiggle toes.
Pretend to cast the line.
Sway 'rod' from side to side.
Keep 'rod' still on "fish..." then lift arms up high.

We're fishing for a fish,
Fishing for a fish by the sea.
With a rod in one hand,
Our toes in the sand.
Cast the line out to sea.

Fishing, we're fishing,
Will we catch a big fish for our tea?
Fishing, we're fishing,
Will we catch a big fish for our tea?

(Spoken)
Swish, swish, swish, SNAP!
How many fish did you catch for your tea?

mmm**mmm**

Moving!

Try this ...

1-2 yrs

◆ Walk with, or carry baby to the beat of the song.

Be still for a moment, then continue as actions describe.

Say "hello" to another baby.

Continue as actions describe.

2-4 yrs

◆ Walk with the music, then be still for a moment.

Continue with other verses.

◆ Walk with a friend, holding hands.

When you stop, acknowledge a 'new' friend. Move with the new friend for the next verse.

◆ In between each verse choose a different instrumental sound.

◆ Replace the last line with "What can you see?" Encourage children to respond.

◆ Show them pictures and make different vocal sounds to:

Crabs / Rockpools / Ice-cream/ Sand / Boats / Sand castles / Fish / Donkeys /

People swimming etc.

Walking by the seaside,
Walking by the sea.
Walking by the seaside,
Walking by the sea.

Walking by the seaside,
Walking by the sea.
Walking by the seaside,
Walking by the sea.

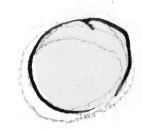

Running, running, running on the sand,
Running, running, running on the sand.
Running, running, running on the sand,
Running, running, running on the sand.

Jumping over waves,
Jumping over waves.
Jumping over waves,
Jumping over waves.

Splashing in the water,
Splashing in the sea.
Splashing in the water,
Splashing in the sea.

Playing Together

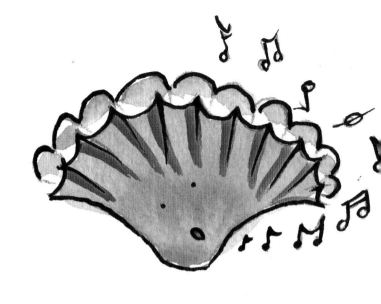

Try this ...

1-2 yrs

◆ Play an instrument to the melody of this song.
When the melody stops, be really quiet.

◆ Play only at the end of this song. Play quietly or loudly, fast or slow.

2-4 yrs

◆ Encourage the children to take turns to 'conduct' the group by
moving one hand up and down to the regular beat.

◆ Split the children into two groups.
One half "la's" the melody. The other half plays their instrument.
Then change places.

◆ Create different sounds with instruments at the end of the song.
Substitute "instruments" for "seashells".

Seashells, seashells,
Sing about the sea.
Tell me about the ocean,
Tell me about the sea.

A sailor went to sea sea sea,
To see what he could see see see.
But all that he could see see see,
Was the bottom of the deep blue
sea sea sea.

31

Musical Games

Try this ...

1-2 yrs
◆ Bounce baby from side to side.
Do a bigger bounce for "Up".
On "SPLASH!" push baby gently to one side with lots of splash sounds.
◆ Change 'dolphins' to the name of a child, or "babies".

2-4 yrs
◆ A child is chosen to be the fish and curls up on the floor.
All the others are dolphins swimming around.
The 'fish' jumps up. The 'dolphins' clap hands on "SPLASH!".
◆ The 'dolphins' could have a ribbon each to help them move around.
Substitute other fish for dolphins, or children's names.

Dolphins in the water,
Dolphins in the sea.
Up jumps the big fish,
Up jumps she!

S P L A S H !

A moment to listen

Try this ...

Skye Boat Song on trumpet

1-2 yrs
◆ Sit quietly and enjoy the music with your baby.
◆ Encourage movement as they listen, and observe any sounds your toddler makes.

2-4 yrs
◆ Sit quietly and listen to the music together.
◆ Ask questions after listening such as,
"Is it quiet?"
"Is it loud?"
"Can you pretend to play along?"
◆ Encourage children to draw what they hear on paper.

A lullaby, shhh...

Try this ...

1-2 yrs
◆ Make lots of quiet sounds such as "shhh".
Stroke your child's head throughout the song.
Lie down and listen together.
Hum the melody to your baby.

◆ Play "PEEKABOO!" with your baby with your fingers as fish.

2-4 yrs
◆ Put arms down for the sun, then up for the moon.
Put fingers to lips, then place your hands by your head.
Put arms up, then wiggle fingers.
Put fingers to lips, then place your hands by your head.

◆ Show 1, 2, then 3 fingers.
Hide all fingers, put hand over eyes. Say "BOO!"

The sun goes down, the moon is high.
The fish are tired, they go to sleep.
Good night, sleep tight.

The stars shine bright, over the sea.
The fish are tired, they go to sleep.
Good night, sleep tight.

1 fish,
2 fish,
3 fish play hide and seek.
Swish, swish, swish,
Where are you?

BOO!

Goodbye!

Try this ...

1-2 yrs
◆ Sway gently sideways for goodbye.
Then wave hands.
Do actions as described.

2-4 yrs
◆ Wave hands goodbye.

Sing goodbye, goodbye,
Sing goodbye, goodbye,
Sing goodbye, goodbye to you.

Can you clap your hands...

Sing goodbye, goodbye,
Sing goodbye, goodbye,
Sing goodbye, goodbye to you.

39

CD Tracks

Instruments played ...

Piano
Guitar
Kantale
Ukulele
Vocals
Calabash
Caxixi
Cymbols
Ocean drum
Trumpet
Percussion
Special effects

All about animals
1. In our house
2. Sing hello together
3. Blue bird
4. The farmer's on the farm
5. Walking on the green grass
6. Clip clop goes the pony
7. Pass the instruments
8. Play together
9. The mouse crept ...
10. 5 little monkeys
11. Clementi's Sonatina in G major
12. Where is the owl
13. Sing goodbye

All about water
14. In our house
15. Sing hello, hello
16. Bubbles
17. Water in the air
18. We're fishing for a fish
19. Walking by the seaside
20. A sailor went to sea sea sea
21. Seashells
22. Dolphins in the water
23. The Skye boat song
24. The sun goes down
25. 1 little fish
26. Sing goodbye, goodbye
27-45. Instrumental